Rainbow

Also by Barrie Wade
Conkers
Barley Barley

Rainbow

Poems by Barrie Wade

Illustrated by Annabel Large

Oxford University Press
Oxford New York Toronto

Oxford University Press, Walton Street, Oxford OX2 6DP

Oxford New York Toronto
Delhi Bombay Calcutta Madras Karachi
Kuala Lumpur Singapore Hong Kong Tokyo
Nairobi Dar es Salaam Cape Town
Melbourne Auckland Madrid

and associated companies in
Berlin Ibadan

Oxford is a trade mark of Oxford University Press

Text copyright © Barrie Wade 1995
Illustrations copyright © Annabel Large 1995
First published 1995

A CIP catalogue record for this book is available from the
British Library

ISBN 0 19 276124 2

Printed and bound in Great Britain by
Butler & Tanner Ltd, Frome and London

For Ann, Rowena, Miranda, and Imogen

Contents

Rainbow

Yesterday
my grandma said,
'there's all the colours of the rainbow
in your school.'

I knew that she was wrong.

We have no orange people,

nor green nor blue,

and you couldn't say
that Tony Wong was yellow,

more a pale and liquid gold
like corn ripening
under autumn sun.

You could say Ingrid
is close to white
with skin you can nearly see through;

Merle's is sleek and polished black,
lovely as a glossy plum,

but nobody is indigo or violet.

I am the only one
that turns red on a sunny day,

but mostly I am pinky grey
and so that doesn't count.

Today we went outside
measuring our playground.

'Give me your hand,' said Rashid.
Ahmed held his,
then Marita, Marvin, May Ling,
Yana, Zamato, Peter and the rest.

We found our playground is
exactly thirty children wide

and now we're working out
how many it would take
to go right round the earth.

We painted our own pictures
and our teacher put them on the wall.

Underneath she wrote:
**Friendship between children is like a rainbow.
It stretches right across our world**.

So after all my gran was right.

Shadow-Me-Shadow

Skit scat copycat
you can't catch me,
but Shadow-me-shadow
you can't break free.

When golden sunbeams
shimmer down the air,
Shadow-me-shadow
you're always there.

When silver moonbeams
slide through the dark,
Shadow-me-shadow
you leave your faint mark.

When the dim lamplight
flickers on the wall,
Shadow-me-shadow
your ghost comes to call.

When the bright firelight
blazes from the hearth,
Shadow-me-shadow
you dance your warpath.

Skit scat copycat
you can't catch me,
but Shadow-me-shadow
you can't break free.

Morning Break

Clouds in sky's playground
pause to pull faces at me
through sunbeam railings.

Child Hates

I hate to be lonely
as lonely can be,
sniffing cold air
like a fox running free.

I hate to be spiteful
as spiteful can be,
feeling wings flutter
and tear inside me.

I hate to be empty
as empty can be,
gazing blank-eyed at
an endless grey sea.

I hate to be timid
as timid can be,
listening for breathing
of ghosts in the tree.

I hate to be gloomy
as gloomy can be,
tasting the ashes
of life's misery.

Child Loves

I love to be lively
as lively can be,
hearing swift rivers
surge down to the sea.

I love to be peaceful
as peaceful can be,
touching a petal
as light as a bee.

I love to be dreamy
as dreamy can be,
watching cloud pictures
float high over me.

I love to be daring
as daring can be,
running up hilltops
where fragrance blows free.

I love to be joyful
as joyful can be,
tasting bright fruits from
the sweet apple tree.

Come-day Go-day

Here comes Monday.
School has begun day.
It's a hit-and-run day.
What a very glum day.
There goes Monday.

Here comes Tuesday.
Chase away the blues day.
You can pick and choose day.
Let's have a snooze day.
There goes Tuesday.

Here comes Wednesday.
Tying up the ends day.
It's a let's pretends day.
Drive you round the bends day.
There goes Wednesday.

Here comes Thursday.
It's a his and hers day.
Everyone prefers day.
Quite a connoisseur's day.
There goes Thursday.

Here comes Friday.
Knocks you sky-high day.
Sing a lullaby day.
Get some shuteye day.
There goes Friday.

Here comes Saturday.
Let's have a natter day.
Run and scatter day.
Mad as a hatter day.
There goes Saturday.

Here comes Sunday.
Meat overdone day.
Let's have some fun day.
Forget about Monday.
There goes Sunday.

Forgetting

On Monday I forgot my dinner money –
left it on the table.
Teacher said, 'It's too much to expect Brian
to make a good start to the week.'

On Tuesday I forgot my library book –
left it in my bedroom.
Teacher said, 'Brian, it's a wonder you brought
your head to school. Maybe you didn't!'

On Wednesday I forgot my pen –
left it in my drawer.
Teacher said, 'Brian, your skull is a colander.
You must have brain drain – or Brian drain!'

On Thursday I forgot my football boots –
left them in the kitchen.
Teacher said, 'Brian, you should knot your
     handkerchief –
or shoelaces. Falling over might remind you.'

On Friday I forgot nothing at all.
I felt good until
Teacher said, 'Quiet everybody. Brian is
trying hard to remember what he's forgotten.'

I remember everything that people
say to me.
Mum tells me never to forget
my teacher has no children of her own.

Lonely Child

A lonely child is like a cloud
imprisoned in sky's empty vault;
and when its rain begins to fall,
the drops are tears of pain and salt;
and when the salt is dried again,
it lies in dead cold grates like ash;
and when the dust is blown in air,
it drops on skin an ugly rash;
and when that rash begins to sting,
its pain is sleetstorms driven wild;
and when sky's wilderness is whipped,
each cloud is like a lonely child.

Telling

Tell-tale tit!
Your tongue will split
and all the dogs
will have a little bit.

I did not tell
and held shame's flood behind my eyes,
when Danny Young and Micky Price
stole my lunch and ate my cake,
thumped my arms and made them ache.

If you tell,
we'll give you hell
and squash your face
all over the place.

I did not tell
for ash of anguish parched my tongue,
when hulking, grinning Danny Young
snatched my anorak by the hood
and trod it deeply into mud.

If you tell,
I'll give you hell
and squash your face
all over the place.

I did not tell
though flames of anger scorched my face,
when oily, rat-eyed Micky Price
gave my work his admiring look,
then squirted ink across my book.

If you tell,
I'll give you hell
and squash your face
all over the place.

I only told
with rocks of sorrow in my heart,
when Danny Young and Micky hurt
poor Lee, although he swore he'd lost
the coins that getting past them cost.

Tell-tale tit!
Your tongue will split
and all the dogs
will have a little bit.

After I told
and Dan and Micky left our school,
the sun continued shining still.
Nothing dreadful happened. In fact,
so far my tongue is still intact.

Bully Bill McIllican

Bully Bill McIllican
eats up stones.
Bully Bill McIllican
crunches bones.

If your friends are walking with you,
give him your best smile.
But if you meet him when alone,
Run a MILE!

Susie Maloozie

Susie Maloozie stood up on her chair,
Then climbed to the cupboard-top high in the air.
She folded her arms
And wouldn't come down.
Even our teacher couldn't reach her.

Spangles

Watching passing clouds I float
in sunlit pieces, light as foam
that drifts and tears and separates
beyond the reach of human pain.

Following twigs in streams I skim
down a risky, hopeful current
that briefly lets each new idea
bob at the surface of the brain.

Looking into trees I stir
and shimmer with the light of love,
feel knots of anger, stumps of greed,
soothed by the tender sway of leaves.

Gazing up at stars I whirl
at the further edge of darkness,
bringing the necessary light
to rework a human pattern.

Heron Haiku

A pair of herons
climb up the face of the sky
twitching its eyebrows

Herons

Requiring a long runway
with undercarriage down,
herons lumber in for landing.
Overhead, on escort duty,
terns with angled geometry
flex their bladed wings,

while at the lakeside
inch-long damsel flies,
after playing touch and go with grass,
return with motors set for hovering
and bluetail landing lights switched on –
make their touch-down on to lily pads.

Thaw

In the ice storms of a hardened heart
stand lacy hawthorns in a frozen dream
and sulky robins that will never sing
in granite bushes by a solid stream
while winter screws each to a coiled-up spring.

In the melting of a frozen heart
nod mellow daffodils that dream
and fluting blackbirds that rejoice to sing
in slackened shrubs beside a warbling stream
to welcome love and the returning spring.

Spring Haiku 1

On the pond's soft cheek
waterboatmen twitch like smiles
dimpling the surface.

Spring Haiku 2

Dip and glide and soar –
woodpigeons brush the treetops.
Kisses in springtime.

Signposts

When snowdrops are dangling
their winterwhite bells,
I hear sounds of spring
like deep echoes in wells.

When daffodil trumpets
seem ready to blare,
a few drops of summer
drip golden through air.

When roses lay perfume
on summer-red days,
the cool mists of autumn
creep in with the haze.

When Michaelmas daisies
through pale autumn light
shine their winterblue stars,
the ice is in sight.

Puddles

Rain bounces on the road
and into hollows little rivers flow.
A sharp breeze makes
gloom descend to furrow lakes;
then little storms grow calm,
as sun returns to make the asphalt warm.
Steam rises, surface dries
and each last gasp of breeze gives up and dies.

Each landlocked shallow shrinks
as round its edge the sunshine drinks
but, as the clouds sail past,
each mirror frames them in its polished glass –
reflecting for a while the sum
of what they were and what they will become.

Swallow Haiku

Scissors in the air
that snip and cut out patterns:
swallows on the wing.

Bouncing

Can I stay up late to watch TV?
Can I go to Andy's house for tea?

> 'Ask your father,' says my mum.
> 'Ask your mother,' says my dad.

Can I go to watch the football match?
Can I join the choir at church?

> 'Ask your father,' says my mum.
> 'Ask your mother,' says my dad.

Can I have a kitten for a pet?
Is my T-shirt ironed yet?

> 'Ask your father,' says my mum.
> 'Ask your mother,' says my dad.

Can I have a floppy-eared bunny?
Can I have some pocket money?

> 'Ask your father,' says my mum.
> 'Ask your mother,' says my dad.

Can I learn to play the violin?
Who put my comics in the bin?

> 'Ask your father,' says my mum.
> 'Ask your mother,' says my dad.

Am I only a kind of pingpong ball?
Does anyone here know anything at all?

> 'Ask your father,' says my mum.
> 'Ask your mother,' says my dad.

Crack Another Yolk

At breakfast we scramble to sit
and egg each other on,
cracking yolk after yolk.
To my sister I say, 'You're chicken.'
She says, 'You've an addled head.'
'Look at the sun. He side up,' I say.
'It's enough to make you turn white,' she replies.
'That's a fowl yolk,' I cry,
'and it's one you've poached from me.'
She says, 'You're not eggs actly right.
If you see a leg, then pullet.'

Our mum's become hardboiled to this.
She takes it all with a pinch of salt.

Sensible Shoes

Inside the shop
Mum says

                              she wants sensible shoes

not shiny stylish slingbacks

                              she wants sensible shoes

not shiny stylish slingbacks
nor big thick blockerboots

                              she wants sensible shoes

not shiny stylish slingbacks
nor big thick blockerboots
nor pretty little peeptoes

                              she wants sensible shoes

not shiny stylish slingbacks
nor big thick blockerboots
nor pretty little peeptoes
nor tough sporty trainers

                          she wants sensible shoes

not shiny stylish slingbacks
nor big thick blockerboots
nor pretty little peeptoes
nor tough sporty trainers
nor multicoloured moccasins

                          she wants sensible shoes

not shiny stylish slingbacks
nor big thick blockerboots
nor pretty little peeptoes
nor tough sporty trainers
nor multicoloured moccasins
nor glossy green galoshes

                          she wants sensible shoes

not shiny stylish slingbacks
nor big thick blockerboots
nor pretty little peeptoes
nor tough sporty trainers
nor multicoloured moccasins
nor glossy green galoshes
nor clumping clattering clogs.

Outside the shop she says
now you have sensible sh–
OO – and she suddenly
stops short as her
stilletto heel
gets stuck
inside a
pave-
ment
C
R
A
C
K

Do-It-Yourself

and find your own rhyme for each verse

'This room is such a mess!' my mum complained.
'The paint is scratched. The wallpaper is stained.
It looks as if those ceiling tiles will fall
and someone here's been writing on the ___.'

At this my little sister flushed bright red,
but Dad came to her rescue and he said,
'Now then, remember when we fixed those shelves?
This is the same. Let's do it all our ___.'

Dad loves it when we all co-operate,
so Mum agreed to let us decorate.
She bought the paper, paste, and paint from town
and we forgot how soon those shelves fell ___ .

Mum fetched old sheets to cover furniture,
but from her face I saw she was quite sure
that her new carpet would be a disaster
when Dad had filled the ceiling cracks with ___ .

'Don't worry. We'll make absolutely sure,'
said Dad. He draped the chairs and covered floor
and carpet with amazing speed. That day
we thought our grandad must have run ___ .

When we had stripped the walls and smoothed
    the grouts,
we found the clues to Grandad's whereabouts.
My sister recognized him by his feet
and snores that came from underneath a ___ .

Soon after that my little sister, who's a fool,
put ceiling tiles across a bucket, made a stool.
Silly thing! She must have thought that they'd
    support her.
Of course, they broke and she sat in cold ___ .

Mum had picked a yellow paint called 'Daffodil'
and I was allowed to paint the window-sill.
I took great care, but the job was tricky
and the paint flowed thick and fast and ___ .

I carefully fixed up a WET PAINT warning,
but forgot our cat can't read. Next morning
she was stuck on her favourite window-sill,
looking less like a cat than a ___ .

Laughing at my mistake, Dad wiped his eyes
and that's how Grandma had her own surprise
when she came in. Dad swore it never was his plan
to paint that glossy stripe on our beloved ___ .

But Grandma, who's a peaceful soul, unless provoked
went screaming wild. She swiped her stick at Dad
    and poked
the paint tin from his hand, shouting, 'Stupid fellow!
I'll teach you to paint a poor old woman ___ .'

After all that excitement the papering proved dull.
When one strip on the ceiling began to uncurl
Dad shoved it back with a brush – though if he'd
    turned round
he'd have seen the whole piece falling down to the ___ .

'Come along!' cried Dad. 'That's enough mistakes.
Good organization is what it takes.
Let's work as a team. The workers – that's you.
I'll be the boss and tell you what to ___ .'

Mum covered the wallpaper strips with paste.
We carried them over to Dad in haste.
Our dad had the easiest job of all.
He just had to stick them flat on the ___ .

'That's finished,' said Dad, but then came a shout
of panic from Mum, 'We've lost the way out!'
I laughed so much I rolled on the floor.
Our dad had papered over the ___ .

Richard Of York Gave Battle In Vain

Red roses loom large on their shields.
Orange sun glares through mists of the field.
Yellow beams slant from armour of brass.
Green are the spears of yet untrampled grass.
Blue is the unsheathed steel of a sword.
Indigo drains the rich cost of blood.
Violet gathers death's deepening shade.

Fate

In the deep gloom of space my planet spins
In that planet's grey seas my island stands
In that island's harsh rock my town is set
In that town's dreary maze my street runs straight
In that dismal street my playground lies
In that murky playground my school buildings rise
In that dingy school my classroom cowers
In that drab classroom my broken desk totters
In that tumbledown desk my lunchbox sits
In that old, battered box my apple waits
In that wizened apple squirms a fat yellow grub.

Child Alone

Like tides against a rock
they touch then drain away.
They splash and trickle back.
Their liquid voices say
exactly what I lack.

I need the heart that cares,
the mind that understands,
the love that calms all fears,
and reassuring hands
to wipe my salt wet tears.

Learning

Today I learned
how a spider
wraps its silk
around a fly,
makes the web bounce
with urgent tread –
forward, wrap and back
forward, wrap and back.
I watched until
the fly was glued,
the spider still,
the web less taut.

Today I learned
the ringdove's call,
like morse code
from our rooftop,
cuk-cuk-coo –
two short one long.
He kept it up for
ten neck-jerking minutes –
cuk-cuk-coo,
then dipped away
without a backward glance.

Today I learned
that daisies smell
like stale milk.
I picked one,
crushed its hairy stalk
between my fingers
and the fatty stink
lingered rancid
on my skin.

Today I learned
that cats have
tongues like sandpaper.
This tabby gave me
friendly licks
that rasped my fingers,
sent the shivers
spiralling
around my spine.

Today I would have learned
a lot more
but I had to go
to school.

Fly

roused by the haze,
slantwise
on summer days
he makes
his zigzag visits,
first at the corners
of eyes,
then in easy spirals;
finally in zany lines
inscribes his mazes on to air,
rising to his zenith;
afterwards he pauses
and dozes.

The Snail

slow and easily
smooth and leisurely
it slides
silent as a daydream
swaying its spirals of brown fantasy
leaving slender threads for memory
to trace
and follow later

Disco

Our disco blazes
like the sun
on baking sands;
light and heat
pervade,
make our pulses
vibrant.
The beat throbs
into our chests,
thumps in blood,
hammers bone.

Minds have melted
in the heat.
Our gaze
goes to where
the lights are fuzzed
on steamy windows,
each of us
making
our own mirage.

Daddy Asleep

Dulcet, mellow he begins –
drone of a distant bagpipe
breeze gathering in the trees;
then a rumble of rolling boulders
like early warning of avalanche,
wild panic, gruff cacophony – a herd
of pigs in ragged, downhill flight;
a breathless pause –
only the woodman's gate grinds on hinges,
the rasp of his ripsaw steady, rhythmic;
finally, resonant and sonorous,
blares the main blast of fanfare
and it is stentorian.

Daisies

Born in blood,
their bland faces
are yellow open suns
in double-frilled coronas;
crushed they bear
the stale stink of milk
smeared on bottles
left in playground crates;
at dusk, asleep,
their petals clench
to tiny fists
protecting their birthright.

Rain Haiku

Under looming clouds,
oil splashed in the rain flashes
rainbows on my heart.

Hocus Pocus

We use a hocus
it's easy to focus
on weeding a crocus
in the flower bed.

We put away the hocus
its handle will pocus.
Hocus pocus
means 'watch where you tread!'

Hickory, Dickory, Dock

Hickory, dickory, dock,
The mouse ran up the clock.
The clock struck one;
The mouse ran down.
Hickory, dickory, dock.

Hickory, dickory, dock,
He would have had a shock,
If he had run
Up there at noon.
Hickory, dickory, dock.

Piggy on the Railway

Piggy on the railway, picking up stones
Up came an engine, and broke Piggy's bones
Oh, said Piggy, that's not fair –
Oh, said the driver, I don't care.

Last loaf in the breadshop, I'm at the front
In came a lady, with a shove and a grunt.
Whose turn next? the baker said –
Mine, squealed the lady, I want bread.

Whispering in the library, choosing our books
Two porky gentlemen gave us dirty looks
Well, snorted one, snout in the air,
Them noisy children shouldn't be 'ere.

Piggy on the railway, picking up stones
Up came an engine, and broke Piggy's bones
Oh, said Piggy, that's not fair –
Oh, said the driver, I don't care.

Experiment

I am trapped in bed –
sent up to my room for smashing
bottles on the kitchen floor.
I was only finding how many

I could stack into a tower.
I managed six and anyway I
caught one before it touched the tiles
and it was slippery with soap.

I said, 'Mum should have dried them.
Milk bottles are not much use.
They were empty anyway.'
Lips tightened. I was sent up here.

My mum, who teaches science, often says
an animal's ability to be destructive
increases with its intelligence.
Dad says that I am way ahead.

Owl

From furthest dark he hoots defiance
like a naughty child.
That weird and wilful hoo-hoo
ghosts an image on my closed curtain.

I see a tawny head swivel
to bold full face and orange eyes
harden into glass – as close
as if I sat within his tree.

Again he hoots defiance
and a warning.
I feel the tendons flex
and talons tighten round the bark.

I sense the tension
that is coiled ready
for the spring and launch in air.
My arms are spread in silent flight.

The night outside my window holds its breath.
And in my dreams I glide through silent air,
poised on the brink of plunges
that set the mindless furry creatures scurrying.

Night Haiku

A kaleidoscope
is ready to be shaken
as I drift to sleep.

The treestump grows eyes
and flies out at the starlight:
'Whit-too-whoo-too-whoo.'

Along the fence top
a watchful tomcat passes
lightly as a dream.

Light pencils scribble
their crazy, tangled graphics:
moths round the streetlight.

Like molten copper
pouring through hawthorn hedgerows
the fox goes hunting.

As if stars could speak,
shrill at the edge of hearing,
bats use their radar.

I sparkle with dreams:
diamond strings are laid across
my velvet slumber.

There's a Thing in My Room

There's a thing in my room
in the dark well of night.
There's a thing in my room
makes my lips dry with fright.

It is only the honeysuckle
that clings to the wall
whose scent has crept in the window.
It is only a scent, that's all.

There's a thing in my room
in the velvety dark.
There's a thing in my room
whining and moaning. Hark!

It is only the uneasy wind
with frenzy enough for a squall
to rattle the glass in the window.
It is only a sound, that's all.

There's a thing in my room
in the black curtained night.
There's a thing in my room
shining ghostly and white.

It is only the moon's phantom form,
dressed in her silvery shawl,
stepping through a gap in the curtains.
It is only the moon, that's all.

Lullaby

Hush, can you hear
in the thickening deep
the air in the trees
is falling asleep?

Hush, can you see
where the darkening skies
stretch over the sunset
and close heavy eyes?

Hush, can you hear
where the whispering corn
is settling down
and starting to yawn?

Hush, can you see
in the moon's silver beam
the light of the world
beginning to dream?

Hush, can you feel
the whole world give a sigh
and fall fast asleep
to your lullaby?